CONTENTS

Tree-HOUSE comix proudly Presents

DOG MAN
FOR WHOM THE BALL ROLLS

WRITTEN AND ILLUSTRATED BY **DAV PILKEY**

AS GEORGE BEARD AND HAROLD HUTCHINS

WITH COLOR BY JOSE GARIBALDI

graphix

AN IMPRINT OF

SCHOLASTIC

FOR CHARISSE MELOTO, WHO INSPIRES US ALL TO DO GOOD!

Published in the UK by Scholastic Children's Books, 2020
Euston House, 24 Eversholt Street, London, NW1 1DB, UK
A division of Scholastic Limited.

First published in the US by Scholastic Inc., 2019

London ~ New York ~ Toronto ~ Sydney ~ Auckland
Mexico City ~ New Delhi ~ Hong Kong

SCHOLASTIC and associated logos are trademarks
and/or registered trademarks of Scholastic Inc.

ISBN 978 0702 30367 8

A CIP catalogue record for this book is available from the British Library.

Printed and bound in Great Britain by Bell and Bain Ltd, Glasgow

3 5 7 9 10 8 6 4

www.scholastic.co.uk

Edited by Ken Geist
Book design by Dav Pilkey and Phil Falco
Colour by Jose Garibaldi
Colour flatting by Aaron Polk
Publisher: David Saylor

DOG MAN
Behind the Refined sophistication!

Yo, ScooBies!!! It's your old Pals George and Harold!

'Sup?

As you might have heard, we're Supa mature now!

And Deep!

The Thinker

We even got an AWARD for being So cultured!!!

Check it out!

STUDENT AWARD

Our next award...

...is for MATURITY!

Thank You, Thank You!

Now that we're Award Winners, we often get chased by our admirers!

But we Love our Fans...

No Autographs today.

...Which is why we've worked tirelessly...

...to create this **ALL-NEW** Dog Man Graphic novel!!!

Let's review our story thus far, Shall we?

OUR STORY THUS FAR

by Award-Winning Author George Beard

Illustrated by award-winning illustrator Harold Hutchins

Once there was a cop and a police dog...

KA-

...who got hurt in a big explosion!!!

BOOMERS

Wee-ooo-wee-ooo

They were rushed to the hospital...

...where the Doctor had sad, sad news!

Boo-Hoo

Sorry, cop Dude! But your head is dying.

Weak!

Dog Man has three Awesome friends:

ZuZu: world's greatest Poodle

Sarah Hatoff: world's greatest reporter

Chief: world's greatest chief

But there are complications...

Petey: World's most morally conflicted cat

One time, Petey tried to make an evil clone of himself...

Cloning Machine

start

DNA

...But he got a good-hearted son instead.

Papa

Li'L Petey: world's greatest Kitten

Petey tried to make his son become evil...

...but the Power of <u>Good</u> was stronger.

I'm afraid I can't be good. I've been so **BAD** in the past!

It's not about who we've been, Papa...

...It's about who we can become.

If Petey is going to be a good guy...

...he'd better hurry it up!!!

Because three **New** villains just arrived!

Piggy: Boss of "The FLEAS"

Bub: flunky #1

Crunky: Flunky #2

Recently, they got shrunk to the size of **Actual** fleas...

ZAP

...and they could be hiding Anywhere!!!

scratch

scratch

scratch

scratch

Fortunately, Li'l Petey has been living with Dog Man while his Papa is in Cat Jail.

They share their home with a robot named 80-HD.

Together, the three friends have become a family.

A family who fights the forces of BADNESS!

What could possibly go wrong?

CHAPTER 1

Tree-
House
comix
Proudly
Presents

Rise OF THE PLANET OF THE CATS

News

Last night's tragedy was narrowly averted...

...thanks to the **SUPA BUDDIES!**

But the biggest surprise of the night...

...was the heroic bravery...

...of Petey the Cat!

Check him out...

...as he saves this kid from the raging fire!

I'm so **PROUD** of you, Petey!!!

You're a **Hero!**

CUT iT OUT, BiG JiM!!!

Heroes DON'T SNUGGLE!

Sorry, Petey.

18

In related news, Seven dog fugitives Also saved a guy!

The governor was So impressed, She **PARDONED** Them!

Now all Seven dogs are **FREE!**

Isn't that **NICE?**

Gee, that **IS** nice!!!

WHAT'S **Nice** ABOUT iT???

THOSE DOGS GOT SeT Free--- but **I'm** STill Locked up!!!

WHeRe's **MY** PARDON???

Yeah!

Petey's **RiGHT!**

Why do **DOGS** get Special Treatment?

I'm Hangry!

20

* French for: "Fight the Power, Baby!!!"

Meanwhile...

STOP, Thief!!

No Way!

chief

chief

HUFF
PUFF
HUFF

chief

WAIT UP!!!

HUFF PUFF
HUFF
PUFF

chief

It's no use, Dog Man. I can't run anymore!

HUFF
PUFF

chief

23

Okay, Okay...

Grrr

...I give up!!!

But --- before you take me to jail...

...I've got something for you!!!

It's here inside my shirt!!!

OH!

Sniff
Sniff

STEP 1.
First, place your left hand inside the dotted lines marked "Left hand here." Hold the book open FLAT!

STEP 2:
Grasp the right-hand page with your thumb and index finger (inside the dotted lines marked "Right Thumb Here").

STEP 3:
Now QUICKLY flip the right-hand page back and forth until the picture appears to be Animated.

(for extra fun, try adding your own sound-effects!)

O.RAMA

Remember,

while you are flipping,
be sure you can see
the image on page **29**
AND the image on page **31**.

If you flip quickly,
the two pictures will
start to look like
one **Animated** cartoon!

Don't forget to
add your own
sound-effects!

Left
hand here.

Who wazza bally wally?

Bazza wazza bally wall?

Who's a good doggy wazza bally wally?

Right Thumb here.

Who
Wazza
bally
wally?

Bazza
Wazza
bally
wall?

Who's a
good
doggy
Wazza
bally
wally?

Are ya **Ready?**

Let's RoLL!

Roll Roll Roll Roll Roll   Roll Roll Roll Roll Ro...

Meanwhile...

Oh boy, this is gonna be **Great!**

Dog Man's gonna catch the crook all by himself...

...now **everybody** will know what an Awesome cop he is!

33

WHAT iS WRONG WiTH YOU???

That's The THiRD Time This Week!

A BAD GUY ROLLS a BALL, YOU CHASE iT, And he GeTS AWAY!

GO HOME, DOG MAN!

Tree-
HOUSE
comix
proudly
Presents

Chapter 2

Behavioral Modification Therapy

Whisper
whisper
whisper

Okay, Dog Man. 80-HD and I are going to Teach you to **FOCUS!**

FLIP FLOP FLIP FLOP

We'll use these flash cards we made.

Every time you stay Focused, you get a <u>treat</u>!

But if you mess up, there's a <u>Penalty</u>!

You'll have to take a **bath!**

splish splash

FLiP FLOP FLi

This might be a hard one.

NO, DOG MAN!

GRRRR

Petey is my Papa, Remember?

He's a good guy! You have to give him a chance!!!

That's better!!!

Lick Lick
Lick

43

And Later...

SCRUB SCRUB SCRUB

...and after that...

SCRUB SCRUB SCRUB

...and so on...
...and so on...
...and so on...

FLIP-O-RAMA

Left hand here.

The good...

...the bad...

...and the sudsy!!!

Right Thumb here.

The
good...

...the
bad...

...and
the
Sudsy!!!

Much, **MUCH** Later...

This is Taking a Lot Longer Than I thought it would.

SCRUB SCRUB SCRUB

But we can't give up, Dog Man!

We always gotta Keep trying!!!

And so...

SPLASH!

Dog Man

SCRUB SCRUB SCRUB

SPLASH!

Dog Man

SCRUB SCRUB SCRUB

SPLASH!

Dog Man

SCRUB SCRUB SCRUB

Tree-
House
comix
Proudly
Presents

CHAPTER 3

TO HECK WITH THE PLANET OF THE CATS

Cat Jail

by the award-winning Award winners,

George Beard & Harold Hutchins

Meanwhile...

MY FELLOW FELINES...

Cat Jail

...NO ANIMAL HAS MORE LIBERTY THAN THE CAT!

THE CAT IS THE BEST ANARCHIST!!!

YEAH!

We Agree!

What's an anarchist?

Beats me!

But we have buried our **Mess** for too Long!!!

WE MUST UNITE!

But, Piggy, ever since we joined **the FLEAS...**

...it's been one **DISASTER** after another!

And now we're so small, we can fit on a cat's whisker!

WHAT'S YOUR POINT?

Let's **QUIT!** I'm **HUNGRY!**

Me too!

We CAN'T QUIT **NOW!** I've got a **NEW** PLAN!

If we can Reach Petey's ear, I can **HYPNOTIZE** him!!!

Then we can mold him into whatever we desire!!!

How about a Pizza?

or a cheeseburger!

Or a big bag of miniature marshmallows!

Or a **CHOCOLATE CUPCAKE** with **SPRINKLES!**

SLAP!

58

And So...

PETEY'S
SECRET
Lab

Lab
Sweet
Lab

Kid-
Sized
Furniture

same day
delivery

PETEY'S
SECRET
Lab

Luke and
Andrew's
Furniture

MARKET

Fruit

Market

Art
Supplies

Toys

Market

FLUFF FLUFF FLUFF

Dog man

GUESS WHO JUST GOT—

Well? Isn't it???

But, Papa, what about Dog Man and 80-HD?

Aw, don't worry about them! They have eAch other!

And now, **we** have each other, too!

oh.

So come on! **Let's GO!!!**

LET GO OF MY LEG!

Look, I appreciate your help while I was in Jail...

...But I'm free now. This is **MY KID!**

He needs to be with **ME!**

You're gonna have to let him go!!!

You **DO** want to live with me, don't you?

Yeah, I guess so.

Well, you don't seem too **HAPPY** about it!

Can Dog Man and 80-HD come and live with us?

No, they can't. It's just gonna be you and me from now on!

Hey, Papa! Look at the cute flowers!

Those aren't flowers. Those are WEEDS!

Oh.

Hey, Papa! Look at the pretty river!

71

CHAPTER 5

A good Dose of Reality

74

75

PLOP!

YOU'RE SLEEPING IN HERE AND THAT'S **FINAL!**

Lick

FLip
FLip
FLip

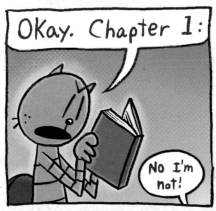

Okay. Chapter 1:

No I'm not!

ALRiGHT, FiNE!
If You're Going
To AcT Like ThAt...

...Then NO BedTime
STORY FoR YOU!

But then...

Hey, Papa, How come Dog Man and 80-HD can't live with us?

Because they **CAN'T!**

Why?

Because it just Wouldn't work out!

Why?

Because I'm SMART And They're a couple of **BONEHEADS!**

Why?

WOULD YOU CUT THAT OUT?!!?

Why?

79

Look, Kid— I'm trying to be good to you.

I wanna give you what **I NEVER HAD!**

When I was a kid, my Papa didn't care about me at all!

He took off and left my mom and me all alone!

He did?

Yep. And I never saw him again.

Hey, I know!

Let's find him!

Are you **CRAZY?** I never wanna see that guy again!

But maybe he's sorry, Papa. Maybe he **changed!**

Look, I know you think everybody is a good guy deep down inside...

81

...I'm just tryin' to protect ya!

Now go to sleep.

G'night, Papa.

GOOD NiGhT, Dog MAN And 80-HD!!!

Petey's secret Lab

WHAT'S THE BIG IDEA?

I thought I told you guys to Let go!!!

Hi, fellas!

Petey's Secret Lab

YOU GET BACK INTO BED RIGHT NOW!!!

Petey's Secret Lab

Alright, listen up, you two...

... Maybe we can work something out.

Right
Thumb
here.

CHAPTER 6

A Buncha Stuff That Happened Next

Meanwhile, back at Cat Jail...

...Big Jim was getting ready for bed.

Hey!

How come we hAve to carry you, Piggy?

Because I'm the **BRAINS** of this Squad!

I can't waste my energy on menial tasks like **WALKING!**

Now **BUZZ OFF** while I work my **MAGIC!**

But how are you gonna do it, Piggy?

How are you gonna turn him into a cupcake?

I'M NOT GONNA TURN HIM INTO A CUPCAKE!!!

Wow! I'm feeling **Subvegetables!**

You shall obey our every command!

Hey! I'm gonna obey these weird voices in my head!!!

Hey, Crunky! I just Got an idea!!!

C'mon!

98

Petey's
secret
LaB

105

Thanks, 80-HD! I'm gonna go back to sleep!

When you find my Grampa, bring him back here, okay?

As a hopeful hero pierces the twilight...

...A Nefarious **NEW** villain Schemes in the Shadows.

RoBo-Time INdustries

And what **New** evil plans are up his newly pressed sleeves?

Who is this New Newcomer???

I'm NOT New!!!

It's Me, Dr. Scum! I was in the First book, Remember?

Oh yeah. Sorry.

Anyway, I've been designing an army of evil Robots!!!

I call them CRIME CRABS!

They're Powerful enough to destroy the earth...

... but can they defeat Dog Man?

That morning before breakfast...

Petey and his son started building a new creation:

The Robo-Rat 2000.

Are you finished building that mecha-endoskeleton?

Almost. I Just have to Attach the cables.

Meanwhile...

Hello, I'm Sarah Hatoff with the News.

Today I'm gonna interview Chief!

chief

Thanks, Sarah. It's a **GREAT** Day for the city...

chief

...Because Dog Man has finally learned how to **FOCUS!**

Ya mean he doesn't go **BONKERS** when ya roll a ball anymore?

Nope! Allow me to demonstrate!

chief

Meanwhile, at Cat Jail...

Hey, Bub!

What did you whisper into this cat's ear last night?

Well, my friend, There's an old saying:

"If you Turn a cat into a cupcake, you'll eat for a day.

But if you turn a cat into a cupcake-themed Superhero...

123

124

CHAPTER 8

The OLd MaN And the Sea-Food Crackers

Meanwhile...

Petey's Secret LaB

HeY! WHAT ARE you doinG?!!?

I'm making a book for my friend, FLippy!

FLiPPY2
ELectRic
Boogaloo

128

PPPBBT!

WHAT ARE YA Tryin' to Do, Poison ME?

WHO TAUGHT you HOW to Cook?

Meanwhile...

You need to **LET ME DOWN!**

But, Piggy, You're my new best friend!

I'll **NEVER** Let you down, buddy!

NO! I MEAN **PUT ME DOWN!!!**

But it's not nice to put people down!!!

LOOK, DARYL, I've HAD JUST ABOUT ENOUGH OF—

Wait a minute...

...Maybe this isn't such a bad idea after all!

With **MY** Brains and **YOUR** wings...

...we could be an **UNBEATABLE TEAM!**

WOW! Just Like **SUPERHEROES!**

WAIT, what?

We'll spread Sunshine and Joy wherever we go!!!

NO WE WON'T!!!

Meanwhile...

I'VE DONE IT!!!

ROBO-Time INDUSTRIES

I've finally finished building my army of BURGLe BALLS!!!

Now it is time To **UNLEASH** Them!

Is everyone ready?

Door opener

CLick

Door opener

GOOD! Let's ROLL!!!

138

CHAPTER 9
Burgle Balls Attack

HEY! What's Going on down here?

We're building the Robo-Rat 2000!!!

Hmm — Let me guess:

YOU'RE the SMART one with All the IDEAS...

...and HE'S the MOOCH who's Riding on YOUR COATTAILS!

C'mon! Haven't you ever wondered why your tail is **ROUND** at the end...

...and his tail is **FLAT???**

Go on, tell him what happened!

KNOCK it OFF, DAD!!!

Why? Are you afraid he won't love you anymore...

...when he finds out what a **LOSER** you really are?!!?

...And DoG Man can't stop me! **MWAH HA HA!**

DoG Man! There's a **NEW** Villain in Town!

I'm Not New!

You must stop this **NEW** threat to Society!

Come on! I was in the First Book!

Go catch the new bAd guy!!!

Seriously! I had a really big Role in Chapter 2!!!

And so...

COPS

CHAPTER 10

DO GOOD

Maturity Award Winner
By George Beard

Maturity Award Winner
and Harold Hutchins

151

And So...

Here they come, Papa!

If we're gonna stop those guys...

...we all have to work together!

I'll be Right bAck!

PLUP

Knock Knock
Knock

You're a good boy, Dog Man...

...But that doesn't mean very much.

Look around.

This city is **Filled** with good people...

...but none of them are **DOING** Anything!

It's not enough to just **BE GOOD.**

We gotta **DO GOOD!**

Even if thinGs get **SCARY!!!**

Even if we face **BATHTIME...**

...or a <u>Thousand</u> Bathtimes...

...**EViL SHALL NOT PREVAiL!**

BECAUSE WE'RE NOT Just GonnA **BE GOOD...**

WE'RE GONNA **DO GOOD!**

Gee, I sure wish
80-HD WAS—

-here.

Okay, Papa! Get Ready!!!

Here Come The SUPA BUDDIES!

GRRRRRR!

RUFF RUFF RUFF

RUFF RUFF RUFF

FLIP, BABY, FLIP!

Left hand here.

Right
Thumb
here.

Tree-House Comix Proudly Presents

Chapter 11
The Very Hangry Raterpillar

Soon, the Very Hangry Raterpillar chased the last remaining Burgle Ball...

... straight to Dr. Scum's Laboratory.

RoBo-Time Industries

GULP!

RATS! All of my Burgle Balls got eaten up!!!

But No worries! That Raterpillar is No match for...

167

The CoLoSSAL-Bot 2000 attacked...

...and the fight was **ON!**

FLiP iT—DON'T RiP iT!

Left hand here.

Right
Thumb
here.

The battle was intense, but fortunately...

...The Very Hangry Raterpillar...

...had an appetite...

...for **DESTRUCTION!!!**

CHAPTER 12

A Farewell to Arms

Petey and the very Hangry Raterpillar were now encased in a charcoal **TOMB...**

MWAH HA HA HA HA!!!

...and nearly everyone on the street below was <u>Horrified!</u>

Don't worry, nearly everyone...

I think I know what's going to happen!

whisper whisper whisper

176

177

Meanwhile...

Okay, Daryl...

SPECIAL Exhibit
THE HOPE
MOOD RING
RAre 'n' Ancient
WARNING: MAY BE CURSED!!!

MUSEUM

...here's the plan:

You're going to lower me down into that museum...

...and I'm going to steal the world-famous "Hope Mood Ring"!

But, Piggy—we can't steal! We're the **Friendly Friends!**

178

The Terrified cries for help echoed across the rooftops...

...and fell upon the ears of a hungry, hungry hero!

As the soft, pink dusk of twilight blankets the city...

...One vigilant soul heeds the sounds of despair...

HELP! HELP!

...And bravely responds.

Masked in the deep shadows of the surrendering sun...

...and armed only with an unquenchable appetite...

...for cupcakes...

SAL'S CUPCAKE Kitchen

...Our spunky spartan of sprinkles barges forth where even the most valiant fear to tiptoe!

Meanwhile, off in the distance, encased in a silent Sepulchre of cinders...

... a Startling transmogrification...

...Crackles to Life from its Carbon Chrysalis.

CRACK!

POP

Aw, come on!!!

188

191

Hey, look! That cupcake-themed superhero just captured the new villain!!!

How'd ya do it?

Well, I—

PLOP!

And Look! He just Captured **PiGGY!**

And he's recovered the stolen **HOPE MOOD RiNG!!!**

Gee, it's too bad he didn't capture **ALL** of the FLEAS!!!

Yeah! I wonder whatever happened to Crunky and Bub?

Hmmm—

scratch scratch

Here they are!

Did we miss anything???

Ya sure did! Commander Cupcake just solved the crimes of the century!!!

HOORAY FOR COMMANDER CUPCAKE!!!

Wait, what?

Okay, so let me get this straight...

Nom Nom Nom

You just eat cupcakes? That's **ALL** you do?

Yep!

HOW IS THAT A SUPERPOWER??

Never Question a Cupcake. For its Powers are delicious forever. Amen.

THAT DOESN'T EVEN MAKE SENSE!!!

Nom Nom

199

What's wrong, Papa?

It's NOT FAIR! We did all of the work...

...and that cupcake GUY got all the **CREDIT!**

It doesn't matter, Papa. Everything still worked out okay!

Oh yeah, I forgot! You're "Mr. Rainbows and Unicorns"!!!

And Lollypops!

ALRight, be my Guest! Keep your head up there in the stars!!!

The only Problem is, there's a Lotta **MUD** down there, PaL!

Hey, Look!

My comics.

He took everything...

...but he didn't want my comics.

Let's Go.

Where?

You're gonna stay at Dog Man's house this weekend, Remember?

But, Papa—

NO! We made a promise and we're Gonna keep it!!!

And so...

213

You wanna know something, kid?

What, Papa?

This world has a lot of problems...

...But it could never be a horrible place...

... because you're in it.

I'll come back on Sunday night to pick you up, okay?

Hey, Papa- You should stay with us this weekend!

No way! I'm Going home! I've Got **BIG PLANS** for that place!

But you don't have a bed to sleep in. Or a Pillow. Or a blanket!

Sure I do! Our Lab has **TONS** of secret rooms **FILLED** with cool stuff!

Now **SCRAM!** Go have fun!!!

Okay! Bye, Papa!

RUFF RUFF RUFF

Flip Flop Flip Flop

DOG Man

UUU

DOG Man

RUFF RUFF RUFF

FLIP FLOP FLIP FLOP

DOG Man

Pick

Blub
Blub
Blub

The

splish splash splish splash splish splash splish splash

Menu   ☰

COMMANDER CUPCAKE CAPTURES CROOKS BY CONSUMING CARBS!

Move over, Supa Buddies, there's a new superhero in town! Last night, Commander Cupcake amazed the world by single-handedly capturing not only the FLEAS, but an all-new villain named Dr. Scum. When asked to comment, Commander Cupcake said, "Ask not what cupcakes can do for you, ask what YOU can do for cupcakes. Amen." The mayor has declared today COMMANDER CUPCAKE DAY and is encouraging all citizens to help fight crime by eating as many cupcakes as possible.

CAT BURGLAR APPREHENDED

 An elderly cat was caught selling stolen goods out of the back of his rental truck last night. He was charged with possession of stolen property, and totally missing the point of this book.

"Wait," said the elderly cat. "There was a point to this book?"

Menu ☰

BEHIND THE BARS: AN EXCLUSIVE INTERVIEW WITH A NEW VILLAIN

This morning I got a chance to interview Dr. Scum, the newest villain ever!

Q: What's it like being a newcomer to the world of villainy?

A: I'm not new! I was in the first book!

Q. How has your newness affected your outlook on life?

A: I just said I wasn't new! What is WRONG with you??? I was in chapter 2! A LOT!!!

Q. Have you thought about returning for a SECOND shot at world domination?

A: I JUST <u>DID</u> RETURN! THAT <u>WAS</u> MY SECOND ATTEMPT! WHY DON'T YOU PEOPLE LISTEN?!!?

Q: Has the stress of your newness been a—

A: THIS INTERVIEW IS <u>OVER</u>!!!

New Kid in Town

DOG MAN IS GO!

If you thought our adventure was over, you ain't read nothin' yet! An ALL-NEW Dog Man novel is coming SOO͟͟ and it's goi͟͟͟ ͟ ͟BEST ONE ͟ ͟ ͟͟s, we'͟ ͟ ͟IVE S͟ ͟ ͟ ͟he ͟ ͟the ͟ ͟ ͟e! The͟ ͟ to f͟͟͟ a new fri͟ ͟ ͟see and a ͟ ͟ ͟ of them. SPOILER ALERT ͟ ͟ ͟ ͟t hap͟ens when Flippy ͟ psychoki͟ ͟ ͟ ͟ ͟wen͟

Uncle Larry?

Hi, Daryl!

NOTES

by George and Harold

⭐ The title of this book (and the titles of Chapters 8 and 12) were inspired by the books of Ernest Hemingway.

⭐ Panels #2 and #3 from page 50 are direct quotes from <u>For Whom the Bell Tolls</u> by Ernest Hemingway (who was A <u>supa</u> cat lover).

⭐ The Very Hangry Raterpillar was inspired by one of our All-Time favorite books: <u>The Very Hungry Caterpillar</u> by Eric Carle.

⭐ Big Jim was named after a 1970s action figure.

⭐ Harold, who usually only illustrates these books, helped write the story for this one.

⭐ One of the themes of this book was inspired by Harold's favorite short poem:

> Two men looked through prison bars.
> One saw mud. The other, stars.

> — author unknown (but variations are often attributed to Dale Carnegie and/or Reverend Frederick Langbridge)

HOW 2 DRAW COMMANDER CUPCAKE

in 42 Ridiculously easy steps!

PAPA AND the KID

in 39 Ridiculously easy steps!!!

Turn the page to give these two fellas a ride on the back of a **RATTERFLY!!!**

Erase Petey's back Leg →

HOW 2 DRAW DOG MAN

in 26 Ridiculously easy steps!

GET READING W

ITH DAV PILKEY!

ABOUT THE AUTHOR-ILLUSTRATOR

When Dav Pilkey was a kid, he was diagnosed with ADHD, dyslexia, and behavioral problems. Dav was so disruptive in class that his teachers made him sit out in the hall every day. Luckily, Dav loved to draw and make up stories. He spent his time in the hallway creating his own original comic books.

In the second grade, Dav Pilkey made a comic book about a superhero named Captain Underpants. Since then, he has been creating bestselling books that explore fun, positive themes and inspire readers everywhere.

ABOUT THE COLORIST

Jose Garibaldi grew up on the South side of Chicago. As a kid, he was a daydreamer and a doodler, and now it's his full-time job to do both. Jose is a professional illustrator, painter, and cartoonist who has created work for many organizations, including Nickelodeon, MAD Magazine, Cartoon Network, and Disney. He is currently working as a visual development artist on THE EPIC ADVENTURES OF CAPTAIN UNDERPANTS for DreamWorks Animation. He lives in Los Angeles, California, with his wonder dogs, Herman and Spanky.